GIGANTI

Written by *Dee Lillegard*

Illustrated by *CD Hullinger*

CelebrationPress

An Imprint of ScottForesman
A Division of HarperCollinsPublishers

Once there was a giant named
Gigantic George.

2

He lived next to a little town by the sea.

3

Gigantic George was so big, he ate watermelons like raisins.

4

He was so big, he could drink a lake
like a glass of milk.

5

One day Gigantic George sneezed.
He blew some houses down. All of the
townspeople got mad at him.

6

Gigantic George cried. His tears flooded the streets. All of the townspeople shook their heads at him.

Then Gigantic George got the hiccups.
They made everything in the town shake.

8

All the townspeople yelled at him.

Poor Gigantic George! He didn't mean to upset his neighbors. Gigantic George sat by the sea and watched the boats go by. He was very lonely.

10

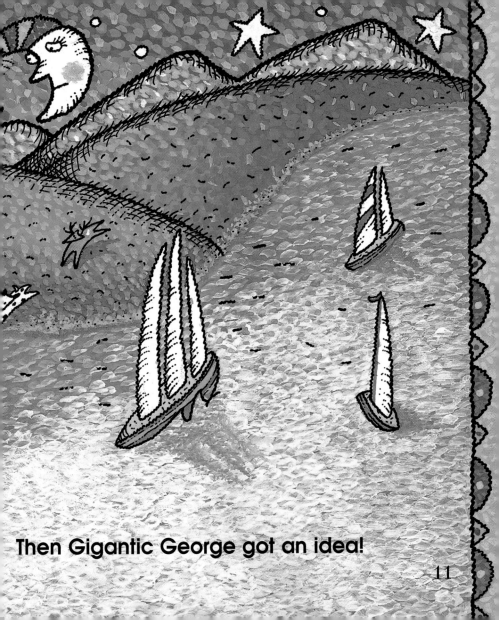

Then Gigantic George got an idea!

He made a gigantic boat so he could sail
away. He passed a little boat. Splash!
He passed a big ship. Splash!

12

At last he came to a big island.
He was very hungry. "Maybe I should stop
here for something to eat," he said. So he
went ashore.

Gigantic George heard a big voice.
"WHO ARE YOU?" it said.

14

He looked up and saw giants his own size.
"Do you want to play with us?" they all asked.

15

Gigantic George knew nobody here would get mad at him. They were all giants, just like him!

16